Schizoaffective Disorder

Ashu Kumawat

Table of contents:

Schizoaffective disorder is a complex and challenging mental illness that affects a person's ability to think, feel, and function. It is a condition that combines the symptoms of schizophrenia and mood disorders such as depression or bipolar disorder. In this chapter, we will provide an overview of schizoaffective disorder, including its symptoms, causes, diagnosis, and treatment.

Schizoaffective disorder is a relatively rare mental illness that affects less than 1% of the population. It typically first presents in the late teens or early adulthood, although it can occur at any age. The exact causes of schizoaffective disorder are not yet fully understood, but it is believed to be the result of a combination of genetic, environmental, and psychological factors.

The symptoms of schizoaffective disorder are characterized by a combination of psychotic symptoms, such as hallucinations and delusions, and mood symptoms, such as depression or mania. The psychotic symptoms can include hearing voices, seeing things that are not there, and having beliefs that are not based on reality. The mood symptoms can include feelings of sadness, hopelessness, or elation, and changes in energy, appetite, and sleep patterns.

The diagnosis of schizoaffective disorder is typically made by a mental health professional, such as a psychiatrist, based on a comprehensive evaluation of the individual's symptoms, medical history, and family history. The evaluation may also include a physical exam, blood tests, and imaging studies to rule out other medical conditions that can cause similar symptoms.

Treatment for schizoaffective disorder typically involves a combination of medication and psychotherapy. Antipsychotic medications are often used to control psychotic symptoms, while mood stabilizers or antidepressants may be used to manage mood symptoms. Psychotherapy, such as cognitive-behavioral therapy or family therapy, can also be beneficial in helping individuals with schizoaffective disorder manage their symptoms, improve their relationships, and enhance their overall quality of life.

Living with schizoaffective disorder can be challenging, and individuals with this condition need to have a strong support system in place. This can include family, friends, mental health professionals, and support groups. It is also important for individuals with schizoaffective disorder to take an active role in their treatment and to work closely with their healthcare providers to develop a personalized treatment plan that meets their specific needs.

One of the most challenging aspects of schizoaffective disorder is the stigma and misunderstanding that surrounds this condition. Many people with schizoaffective disorder may feel isolated or ashamed, and they may be hesitant to seek help due to the fear of being judged or discriminated against. It is important for society as a whole to become more educated about schizoaffective disorder and to work towards reducing the stigma and discrimination associated with this condition.

In conclusion, schizoaffective disorder is a complex and challenging mental illness that can significantly impact a person's quality of life. While there is no cure for schizoaffective disorder, it is a treatable condition, and with the right support and treatment, many individuals with this condition can manage their symptoms and live fulfilling lives. If you or someone you know is struggling with symptoms of schizoaffective disorder, it is important to seek help from a mental health professional who can provide an accurate diagnosis and develop an effective treatment plan. With the right support and treatment, recovery from schizoaffective disorder is possible.

Common Symptoms and Signs of Schizoaffective Disorder

Schizoaffective disorder is a complex and challenging mental illness that can affect a person's ability to think, feel, and function. It is a condition that combines the symptoms of schizophrenia and mood disorders such as depression or bipolar disorder. In this chapter, we will provide an overview of the common symptoms and signs of schizoaffective disorder, including how they may present and impact a person's life.

The symptoms of schizoaffective disorder are characterized by a combination of psychotic symptoms, such as hallucinations and delusions, and mood symptoms, such as depression or mania. These symptoms can vary in severity and frequency and may present differently in different individuals. Some common symptoms and signs of schizoaffective disorder include:

Psychotic symptoms: The most common psychotic symptoms of schizoaffective disorder are hallucinations and delusions. Hallucinations can involve seeing, hearing, or feeling things that are not there. Delusions can involve beliefs that are not based on reality, such as believing that someone is trying to harm you or that you have a special mission.

Mood symptoms: The mood symptoms of schizoaffective disorder can vary depending on the type of mood disorder involved. If depression is present, the person may experience feelings of sadness, hopelessness, or emptiness. If mania is present, the person may experience feelings of euphoria, irritability, or grandiosity.

Disorganized thinking: Schizoaffective disorder can cause disorganized thinking, which can make it difficult for a person to communicate or express themselves clearly. They may have trouble organizing their thoughts or making connections between ideas.

Cognitive impairment: Schizoaffective disorder can also cause cognitive impairment, which can impact a person's ability to think, concentrate, or remember things. They may have difficulty with tasks that require planning or problem-solving.

Social withdrawal: People with schizoaffective disorder may experience social withdrawal, which can make it difficult for them to maintain relationships or participate in social activities. They may isolate themselves from others or feel uncomfortable in social situations.

Changes in behavior: Schizoaffective disorder can also cause changes in behavior, such as increased agitation, restlessness, or impulsivity. They may engage in risky behaviors or act out of character.

Sleep disturbances: Schizoaffective disorder can cause sleep disturbances, such as difficulty falling asleep or staying asleep, or sleeping too much.

Appetite changes: Schizoaffective disorder can also cause appetite changes, such as overeating or loss of appetite, which can lead to weight gain or weight loss.

It is important to note that these symptoms and signs may present differently in different individuals, and not all people with schizoaffective disorder will experience all of these symptoms. Additionally, some of these symptoms may also be present in other mental health conditions, so it is important to seek an accurate diagnosis from a mental health professional.

Living with schizoaffective disorder can be challenging, but with the right support and treatment, many individuals with this condition can manage their symptoms and live fulfilling lives. Treatment typically involves a combination of medication and psychotherapy, such as antipsychotic medications to control psychotic symptoms and mood stabilizers or antidepressants to manage mood symptoms. Psychotherapy can also be beneficial in helping individuals with schizoaffective disorder manage their symptoms, improve their relationships, and enhance their overall quality of life.

In conclusion, the symptoms and signs of schizoaffective disorder can vary in severity and frequency and may present differently in different individuals. Common symptoms and signs include psychotic symptoms, mood symptoms, disorganized thinking, cognitive impairment, social withdrawal, changes in behavior, sleep disturbances, and appetite changes.

The Role of Medication in Treating Schizoaffective Disorder

Medication plays an important role in the treatment of schizoaffective disorder. Schizoaffective disorder is a complex mental illness that involves a combination of psychotic symptoms, such as hallucinations and delusions, and mood symptoms, such as depression or mania. Treatment typically involves a combination of medication and psychotherapy, with medication being an important component of symptom management. In this chapter, we will discuss the different types of medications used in the treatment of schizoaffective disorder, their benefits, and potential side effects.

Antipsychotic Medications

Antipsychotic medications are the cornerstone of treatment for psychotic symptoms in schizoaffective disorder. They work by blocking the effects of dopamine, a neurotransmitter that is thought to be involved in the development of psychotic symptoms. Antipsychotic medications can be divided into two categories: typical and atypical.

Typical antipsychotic medications, also known as first-generation antipsychotics, were the first medications developed to treat psychosis. These medications include chlorpromazine, haloperidol, and fluphenazine. While effective in treating psychotic symptoms, they are associated with a high risk of side effects, such as tardive dyskinesia, a condition characterized by involuntary movements of the face, mouth, and limbs.

Atypical antipsychotic medications, also known as second-generation antipsychotics, were developed in the 1990s and are now the first-line treatment for psychotic symptoms in schizoaffective disorder. These medications include clozapine, risperidone, olanzapine, quetiapine, ziprasidone, aripiprazole, and paliperidone. Atypical antipsychotic medications are associated with a lower risk of side effects, such as tardive dyskinesia, and are more effective in treating both positive and negative symptoms of schizophrenia.

Mood Stabilizers

Mood stabilizers are medications used to manage mood symptoms, such as depression or mania, in schizoaffective disorder. These medications can help stabilize mood and prevent mood swings. The most commonly used mood stabilizers in the treatment of schizoaffective disorder are lithium and valproic acid.

Lithium is a mood stabilizer that has been used for decades to treat bipolar disorder. It works by altering the balance of certain chemicals in the brain, including serotonin and norepinephrine. Lithium can be effective in preventing mood swings and reducing the risk of suicide, but it requires regular blood tests to monitor the levels of the medication in the body and can cause side effects, such as weight gain, tremors, and thyroid problems.

Valproic acid is another mood stabilizer that has been used in the treatment of schizoaffective disorder. It works by increasing the levels of a neurotransmitter called GABA, which helps to regulate mood. Valproic acid can be effective in treating both manic and depressive symptoms but can cause side effects, such as liver problems, weight gain, and tremors.

Antidepressant Medications

Antidepressant medications may be used in the treatment of schizoaffective disorder if depression is a prominent feature of the illness. Antidepressants work by increasing the levels of certain neurotransmitters, such as serotonin and norepinephrine, which can improve mood. The most commonly used antidepressants in the treatment of schizoaffective disorder are selective serotonin reuptake inhibitors (SSRIs) and serotonin-norepinephrine reuptake inhibitors (SNRIs).

Cognitive Behavioral Therapy for Schizoaffective Disorder

Cognitive Behavioral Therapy (CBT) is a type of psychotherapy that is often used in the treatment of schizoaffective disorder. CBT aims to help individuals with schizoaffective disorder identify and change negative thought patterns and behaviors that may be contributing to their symptoms. In this chapter, we will discuss how CBT works, its benefits in the treatment of schizoaffective disorder, and what to expect during CBT sessions.

How CBT Works

CBT is based on the idea that our thoughts, feelings, and behaviors are interconnected and that negative thoughts and behaviors can contribute to symptoms of schizoaffective disorder. CBT aims to help individuals with schizoaffective disorder identify and change these negative thought patterns and behaviors.

During CBT sessions, a therapist will work with the individual to identify negative thoughts and behaviors and challenge them with more positive and realistic thoughts and behaviors. For example, an individual with schizoaffective disorder may have negative thoughts about themselves, such as "I am worthless" or "I will never get better." A therapist using CBT would work with the individual to identify these negative thoughts and challenge them with more positive and realistic thoughts, such as "I am a valuable person" or "I am making progress in my treatment."

CBT may also involve behavioral techniques, such as exposure therapy or relaxation techniques, to help individuals manage symptoms of anxiety or stress that may be contributing to their symptoms.

Benefits of CBT in Schizoaffective Disorder Treatment

CBT is an effective treatment for individuals with schizoaffective disorder. Studies have found that CBT can help reduce symptoms of both psychosis and mood disorders, improve social functioning, and reduce the risk of relapse.

One study published in the American Journal of Psychiatry found that individuals with schizoaffective disorder who received CBT in addition to medication had significantly lower rates of relapse compared to those who received medication alone. Another study published in the Journal of Clinical Psychiatry found that CBT was effective in reducing symptoms of depression and anxiety in individuals with schizoaffective disorder.

In addition to its effectiveness in reducing symptoms, CBT is also a relatively short-term treatment, typically lasting between 12 and 20 sessions. This makes it a convenient and accessible treatment option for individuals with schizoaffective disorder who may have difficulty attending long-term therapy sessions.

What to Expect During CBT Sessions

During CBT sessions, the therapist will work with the individual to identify negative thought patterns and behaviors and challenge them with more positive and realistic thoughts and behaviors. Sessions may also involve behavioral techniques, such as exposure therapy or relaxation techniques, to help manage symptoms of anxiety or stress.

CBT sessions are typically structured and focused on specific goals, such as reducing symptoms of depression or anxiety, improving social functioning, or managing stress. The therapist will work with the individual to develop a treatment plan that addresses their specific needs and goals.

CBT can be delivered in individual or group therapy sessions and can be adapted to the individual's specific needs and preferences. Some individuals may prefer to focus on specific symptoms or issues, while others may prefer a more general approach to treatment.

Conclusion

CBT is a valuable treatment option for individuals with schizoaffective disorder. It can help individuals identify and change negative thought patterns and behaviors, reduce symptoms of both psychosis and mood disorders, improve social functioning, and reduce the risk of relapse. CBT is a relatively short-term treatment that can be adapted to the individual's specific needs and preferences. If you are struggling with symptoms of schizoaffective disorder, CBT may be a helpful addition to your treatment plan.

Dialectical Behavior Therapy for Schizoaffective Disorder

Dialectical Behavior Therapy (DBT) is a type of therapy that is effective in the treatment of schizoaffective disorder. Developed by psychologist Marsha Linehan, DBT combines elements of cognitive behavioral therapy with mindfulness techniques to help individuals with schizoaffective disorder manage their symptoms and improve their quality of life. In this chapter, we will discuss how DBT works, its benefits in the treatment of schizoaffective disorder, and what to expect during DBT sessions.

How DBT Works

DBT is a comprehensive treatment approach that focuses on four main areas: mindfulness, distress tolerance, emotion regulation, and interpersonal effectiveness.

Mindfulness involves developing the ability to focus one's attention on the present moment, without judgment or distraction. In DBT, individuals learn mindfulness techniques such as meditation and breathing exercises to help them stay present and focused on their goals.

Distress tolerance involves learning how to manage intense emotions and distressing situations without resorting to harmful or destructive behaviors. In DBT, individuals learn distress tolerance techniques such as relaxation exercises and self-soothing strategies to help them manage difficult situations.

Emotion regulation involves learning how to identify and manage emotions healthily and effectively. In DBT, individuals learn emotion regulation techniques such as identifying and labeling emotions, challenging negative thoughts and beliefs, and practicing mindfulness to help them regulate their emotions.

Interpersonal effectiveness involves learning how to communicate effectively and maintain healthy relationships with others. In DBT, individuals learn interpersonal effectiveness skills such as assertiveness, active listening, and conflict resolution to help them improve their relationships with others.

Benefits of DBT in Schizoaffective Disorder Treatment

DBT is effective in the treatment of schizoaffective disorder. Studies have found that DBT can help improve symptoms of both psychosis and mood disorders, reduce the risk of self-harm and suicide, and improve the overall quality of life.

One study published in the Journal of Psychiatric Research found that individuals with schizoaffective disorder who received DBT in addition to medication had significantly lower rates of hospitalization and self-harm compared to those who received medication alone. Another study published in the Journal of Consulting and Clinical

Psychology found that DBT was effective in reducing symptoms of depression and anxiety in individuals with schizoaffective disorder.

DBT is also a long-term treatment that can be adapted to the individual's specific needs and preferences. This makes it a convenient and accessible treatment option for individuals with schizoaffective disorder who may need ongoing support and treatment.

What to Expect During DBT Sessions

DBT typically involves both individual therapy sessions and group therapy sessions. In individual therapy sessions, the therapist will work with the individual to develop a treatment plan that addresses their specific needs and goals. During group therapy sessions, individuals will learn and practice DBT skills with others who are also undergoing treatment.

DBT sessions are structured and focused on specific goals, such as improving distress tolerance or developing interpersonal skills. The therapist will work with the individual to develop a treatment plan that addresses their specific needs and preferences.

DBT is a collaborative treatment approach that involves active participation from both the therapist and the individual. Individuals are encouraged to practice DBT skills outside of therapy sessions to help them better manage their symptoms and improve their quality of life.

Conclusion

DBT is a valuable treatment option for individuals with schizoaffective disorder. It combines elements of cognitive behavioral therapy with mindfulness techniques to help individuals manage their symptoms and improve their quality of life. DBT is a long-term treatment that can be adapted to the individual's specific needs and preferences. If you are struggling with symptoms of schizoaffective disorder, DBT may be a helpful addition to your treatment plan.

Family Therapy for Schizoaffective Disorder

Schizoaffective disorder not only affects the individual, but it can also have a significant impact on their family members. Family therapy is a treatment approach that can help individuals with schizoaffective disorder and their families work together to manage the symptoms of the disorder and improve family relationships. In this chapter, we will discuss the benefits of family therapy for schizoaffective disorder, what to expect during family therapy sessions, and how to find a qualified family therapist.

Benefits of Family Therapy for Schizoaffective Disorder

Family therapy is a type of psychotherapy that involves family members working together with a therapist to improve communication and relationships. It can be particularly beneficial for individuals with schizoaffective disorder and their families, as it can help to:

Educate family members about the disorder: Family therapy can provide family members with a better understanding of schizoaffective disorder and its symptoms. This can help to reduce the stigma associated with mental illness and improve family relationships.

Improve communication: Family therapy can help family members to communicate more effectively with one another. This can lead to improved relationships and a better understanding of each other's needs and perspectives.

Develop coping skills: Family therapy can teach family members coping skills to help manage the challenges associated with schizoaffective disorder. This can include strategies for managing stress, developing problem-solving skills, and improving emotional regulation.

Address family dynamics: Family therapy can help to identify and address unhealthy family dynamics that may be contributing to the individual's symptoms. This can include issues such as conflict, enmeshment, or lack of support.

What to Expect During Family Therapy Sessions

Family therapy typically involves regular sessions with a qualified therapist. During these sessions, family members will work together with the therapist to improve communication and relationships and develop coping skills to manage the symptoms of schizoaffective disorder.

Family therapy sessions are structured and focused on specific goals, such as improving communication or addressing specific family dynamics. The therapist will work with the family to develop a treatment plan that addresses their specific needs and preferences.

Family therapy is a collaborative treatment approach that involves active participation from all family members. Individuals are encouraged to practice the skills they learn in therapy outside of therapy sessions to help improve family relationships and manage the symptoms of schizoaffective disorder.

How to Find a Qualified Family Therapist

Finding a qualified family therapist can be challenging, but there are several resources available to help. It is important to find a therapist who has experience working with individuals with schizoaffective disorder and their families.

Here are some tips for finding a qualified family therapist:

Ask for a referral from a mental health professional: If you are already working with a mental health professional, ask them for a referral to a qualified family therapist.

Check with your insurance provider: Check with your insurance provider to see if they cover family therapy services. If they do, they may have a list of qualified therapists in your area.

Use online directories: There are several online directories of mental health professionals that you can use to search for a qualified family therapist in your area.

Ask for recommendations from others: Ask for recommendations from friends, family members, or support groups for individuals with schizoaffective disorder.

Conclusion

Family therapy is a valuable treatment option for individuals with schizoaffective disorder and their families. It can help to improve communication and relationships, develop coping skills, and address unhealthy family dynamics. If you are struggling with schizoaffective disorder, consider including family therapy as part of your treatment plan. Finding a qualified family therapist may take some time and effort, but it can be a worthwhile investment in your mental health and well-being.

Coping Strategies for Managing Schizoaffective Disorder

Schizoaffective disorder can be a challenging mental health condition to manage, but there are coping strategies that individuals can use to improve their symptoms and overall quality of life. In this chapter, we will discuss some effective coping strategies for managing schizoaffective disorder, including lifestyle changes, self-care, and social support.

Lifestyle Changes

Making positive lifestyle changes can help individuals with schizoaffective disorder manage their symptoms and improve their overall well-being. Here are some lifestyle changes that can be particularly helpful:

Establish a routine: Having a daily routine can help individuals with schizoaffective disorder manage their symptoms by providing structure and predictability. This can include establishing regular times for waking up, eating meals, and going to bed.

Exercise regularly: Exercise is effective in reducing symptoms of depression and anxiety, which are common in individuals with schizoaffective disorder. Exercise can also improve overall physical health and well-being.

Practice good sleep hygiene: Getting enough sleep is important for managing symptoms of schizoaffective disorder. This can include establishing a regular sleep schedule, avoiding caffeine and alcohol before bedtime, and creating a relaxing sleep environment.

Self-Care

Self-care involves taking care of one's physical, emotional, and mental health. Here are some self-care strategies that can be particularly helpful for individuals with schizoaffective disorder:

Practice mindfulness: Mindfulness involves focusing on the present moment and accepting one's thoughts and feelings without judgment. This can help individuals with schizoaffective disorder manage stress and improve emotional regulation.

Engage in creative activities: Creative activities such as painting, drawing, or writing can be a helpful outlet for emotions and a way to reduce stress.

Practice relaxation techniques: Relaxation techniques such as deep breathing, progressive muscle relaxation, and guided imagery can help individuals with schizoaffective disorder manage stress and anxiety.

Social Support

Having a strong support system can be important for individuals with schizoaffective disorder. Here are some strategies for building social support:

Join a support group: Support groups for individuals with schizoaffective disorder can provide a safe and supportive environment for sharing experiences and coping strategies.

Build relationships: Building relationships with family members, friends, and coworkers can provide a sense of connection and support.

Seek professional help: Seeking professional help from a therapist or psychiatrist can provide valuable support and guidance for managing symptoms of schizoaffective disorder.

Conclusion

Schizoaffective disorder can be a challenging mental health condition to manage, but there are effective coping strategies that individuals can use to improve their symptoms and overall quality of life. Lifestyle changes such as establishing a routine, exercising regularly, and practicing good sleep hygiene can help manage symptoms. Self-care strategies such as mindfulness, engaging in creative activities, and practicing relaxation techniques can also be helpful. Building social support through support groups, and relationships, and seeking professional help can provide valuable support and guidance for managing symptoms of schizoaffective disorder.

Schizoaffective disorder can be a difficult mental health condition to manage on one's own, and building a support system is crucial for individuals with this condition. In this chapter, we will discuss the importance of building a support system for schizoaffective disorder and provide some strategies for doing so.

Why is a Support System Important for Schizoaffective Disorder?

A support system is a group of individuals who provide emotional, practical, and social support to an individual with a mental health condition. For individuals with schizoaffective disorder, a support system can provide a range of benefits, including:

Emotional support: A support system can provide emotional support during times of stress, anxiety, or depression. They can listen, encourage, and offer reassurance.

Practical support: A support system can provide practical support by helping with daily tasks, such as grocery shopping, cooking, or transportation. They can also help with managing medications or appointments with mental health professionals.

Social support: A support system can provide social support by providing opportunities for socialization and activities, which can help reduce feelings of isolation and loneliness.

Advocacy: A support system can also act as an advocate for the individual with schizoaffective disorder, helping to ensure that their needs are met and their rights are protected.

Strategies for Building a Support System

Family and Friends: Building relationships with family members and friends can be an important part of building a support system. This can involve spending time with loved ones, reaching out for emotional support, and asking for practical help when needed. It is important to communicate openly with family and friends about one's condition and how they can best provide support.

Join a Support Group: Support groups for individuals with schizoaffective disorder can provide a safe and supportive environment for sharing experiences and coping strategies. These groups can be found through mental health organizations, community centers, or online resources.

Seek Professional Help: Seeking professional help from a therapist or psychiatrist can provide valuable support and guidance for managing symptoms of schizoaffective disorder. Mental health professionals can offer strategies for managing symptoms, provide medication management, and help individuals build coping skills.

Online Support: Online support groups and forums can provide a valuable source of support for individuals with schizoaffective disorder who may have difficulty accessing support in person. These resources can provide a sense of community and connection, as well as opportunities to share experiences and receive advice.

Peer Support: Peer support can involve connecting with individuals who have experienced similar struggles with schizoaffective disorder. Peer support can be found through mental health organizations, community centers, or online resources.

Conclusion

Building a support system is crucial for individuals with schizoaffective disorder. A support system can provide emotional, practical, and social support, as well as act as an advocate for the individual with the condition. Strategies for building a support system can include building relationships with family and friends, joining a support group, seeking professional help, accessing online support resources, and seeking out peer support. Building a strong support system can provide a valuable source of support and guidance for managing symptoms of schizoaffective disorder.

Maintaining Relationships with Schizoaffective Disorder

Maintaining relationships can be challenging for individuals with schizoaffective disorder due to the symptoms and challenges associated with the condition. However, having healthy relationships is essential for emotional well-being and overall quality of life. In this chapter, we will discuss some strategies for maintaining relationships with schizoaffective disorder.

Communication

Clear communication is key to maintaining healthy relationships. Individuals with schizoaffective disorder may experience difficulty communicating effectively due to symptoms such as disorganized thoughts or difficulty concentrating. However, it is important to communicate openly with loved ones about one's condition and how it affects them. This can involve explaining symptoms, discussing treatment plans, and expressing one's needs and concerns. Communicating regularly and openly can help prevent misunderstandings and build trust in relationships.

Manage Symptoms

Schizoaffective disorder can be unpredictable and disruptive to daily life, which can affect relationships. It is important to manage symptoms as much as possible to minimize their impact on relationships. This can involve following treatment plans, taking medication as prescribed, attending therapy or support groups, and practicing healthy lifestyle habits such as getting enough sleep and exercise.

Seek Support

Maintaining relationships can be challenging without adequate support. It is important to build a support system that includes friends, family members, mental health professionals, and support groups. Seeking support can help reduce feelings of isolation and provide practical help when needed. It can also help prevent loved ones from feeling overwhelmed or burned out.

Set Realistic Expectations

Schizoaffective disorder can affect an individual's ability to function in certain areas of life, such as work or socializing. It is important to set realistic expectations for oneself and communicate these expectations with loved ones. This can involve discussing limitations or areas of difficulty and working together to find solutions or adaptations.

Practice Self-Care

Self-care is important for everyone, but particularly for individuals with schizoaffective disorder. Practicing self-care can involve engaging in activities that promote relaxation, reduce stress, and improve overall well-being. This can include activities such as yoga, meditation, or journaling.

Recognize the Importance of Relationships

Relationships are an important part of life and contribute to overall well-being. Recognizing the importance of relationships can help motivate individuals to prioritize maintaining them. This can involve setting goals for building and maintaining relationships, seeking support when needed, and practicing effective communication skills.

Conclusion

Maintaining relationships can be challenging for individuals with schizoaffective disorder, but it is possible with the right strategies in place. These strategies can include clear communication, symptom management, seeking support, setting realistic expectations, practicing self-care, and recognizing the importance of relationships. Building and maintaining healthy relationships can contribute to overall emotional well-being and quality of life for individuals with schizoaffective disorder.

Schizoaffective disorder is a mental health condition that is often surrounded by stigma and misconceptions. Many individuals with schizoaffective disorder face shame and discrimination due to their condition, which can lead to feelings of isolation and low self-esteem. However, it is possible to overcome stigma and shame with the right strategies in place. In this chapter, we will discuss ways to overcome stigma and shame in schizoaffective disorder.

Education

One of the most effective ways to combat stigma and misconceptions about schizoaffective disorder is through education. This involves educating oneself and others about the condition and its symptoms, as well as sharing personal experiences with the condition. Education can help break down stereotypes and myths and promote understanding and empathy.

Seek Support

Stigma and shame can be isolating and difficult to cope with alone. It is important to seek support from loved ones, mental health professionals, and support groups. Support can provide a safe and understanding space to share experiences, express emotions, and find practical help and resources.

Challenge Negative Thoughts

Stigma and shame can lead to negative self-talk and beliefs about oneself and one's condition. It is important to challenge these negative thoughts and replace them with more positive and empowering beliefs. This can involve reframing negative thoughts, practicing positive self-talk, and focusing on one's strengths and accomplishments.

Advocate for Yourself

Advocating for oneself involves speaking up for one's needs, rights, and beliefs. This can involve advocating for appropriate treatment and support, educating others about the condition, and challenging discrimination and stigma. Advocating for oneself can help promote self-esteem and empower individuals to take control of their condition and their lives.

Practice Self-Care

Self-care is an essential part of maintaining emotional well-being and managing stigma and shame. Practicing self-care can involve engaging in activities that promote relaxation and stress reduction, such as exercise or meditation. It can also involve setting boundaries, practicing self-compassion, and seeking help when needed.

Connect with Others

Connecting with others who have experienced similar challenges can be a powerful way to overcome stigma and shame. This can involve joining support groups or online communities, volunteering, or participating in advocacy efforts. Connecting with others can help reduce feelings of isolation and promote a sense of community and belonging.

Conclusion

Schizoaffective disorder can be a challenging condition to navigate, particularly in the face of stigma and shame. However, it is possible to overcome these challenges with the right strategies in place. These strategies can include education, seeking support, challenging negative thoughts, advocating for oneself, practicing self-care, and connecting with others. By taking proactive steps to overcome stigma and shame, individuals with schizoaffective disorder can lead fulfilling and meaningful lives.

The Importance of Self-Care in Schizoaffective Disorder

Self-care is an essential component of managing schizoaffective disorder. This mental health condition can be challenging to navigate and can cause significant stress and distress. Therefore, it is essential to prioritize self-care to promote emotional well-being and reduce symptoms of schizoaffective disorder. In this chapter, we will explore the importance of self-care in schizoaffective disorder and provide some practical tips for incorporating self-care into your routine.

Stress Reduction

Schizoaffective disorder can be a stressful condition, which can exacerbate symptoms and impact overall well-being. Therefore, it is essential to engage in activities that promote relaxation and reduce stress. This can involve activities such as yoga, meditation, deep breathing exercises, or taking a warm bath. Engaging in activities that promote relaxation can help reduce anxiety and promote emotional regulation.

Exercise

Exercise is an essential component of self-care for individuals with schizoaffective disorder. Physical activity has been shown to promote the release of endorphins, which are natural mood boosters. Exercise can also promote better sleep, which is essential for managing symptoms of schizoaffective disorder. Aim to engage in regular exercises, such as a daily walk or a fitness class, to promote physical and emotional well-being.

Sleep

Sleep is critical for overall well-being and is particularly important for individuals with schizoaffective disorder. Sleep disruptions can exacerbate symptoms of the condition and can lead to increased stress and anxiety. Therefore, it is essential to prioritize sleep hygiene practices, such as establishing a consistent sleep routine, avoiding screens before bedtime, and creating a calm sleep environment. Aim for 7-9 hours of sleep each night to promote emotional and physical well-being.

Nutrition

Nutrition is an important component of self-care for individuals with schizoaffective disorder. Eating a healthy and balanced diet can promote physical and emotional well-being. Aim to incorporate a variety of whole foods, including fruits, vegetables, lean protein, and whole grains. Avoid consuming too much sugar, caffeine, or alcohol, as these can exacerbate symptoms of the condition and impact sleep and overall well-being.

Social Support

Social support is essential for individuals with schizoaffective disorder. Spending time with loved ones and engaging in social activities can promote emotional regulation and reduce symptoms of the condition. Aim to spend time with friends and family members who are supportive and understanding. Consider joining a support group or online community to connect with others who have experienced similar challenges.

Mindfulness

Mindfulness is a powerful tool for promoting emotional regulation and reducing symptoms of schizoaffective disorder. Mindfulness involves being present at the moment and focusing on one's thoughts and feelings without judgment. Practicing mindfulness can help reduce anxiety and stress and promote emotional well-being. Consider incorporating mindfulness practices, such as mindfulness meditation or mindful breathing exercises, into your daily routine.

In conclusion, self-care is an essential component of managing schizoaffective disorder. Engaging in activities that promote stress reduction, exercise, sleep, nutrition, social support, and mindfulness can promote emotional well-being and reduce symptoms of the condition. Incorporating self-care practices into your routine can take time and effort, but can ultimately promote a sense of control and empowerment over your condition. Work with your mental health provider to develop a self-care plan that works for you and supports your overall well-being.

Schizoaffective disorder is a complex mental health condition that can lead to stress and anxiety in those who are affected by it. The symptoms of the disorder, including hallucinations, delusions, and mood swings, can be extremely distressing and overwhelming. Therefore, people with schizoaffective disorder need to have strategies for managing stress and anxiety.

Several effective techniques can be used to manage stress and anxiety in people with schizoaffective disorder. These include:

Relaxation techniques: Relaxation techniques such as deep breathing, progressive muscle relaxation, and visualization can be very helpful in managing stress and anxiety. These techniques help to reduce muscle tension and promote a sense of calm.

Mindfulness: Mindfulness is the practice of being fully present at the moment and focusing on the present experience without judgment. Mindfulness can help to reduce stress and anxiety by promoting a sense of calm and relaxation.

Exercise: Exercise is an effective way to manage stress and anxiety. Exercise releases endorphins, which are natural mood-boosters. Regular exercise can also help to improve sleep, which is important for managing stress and anxiety.

Cognitive-behavioral therapy: Cognitive-behavioral therapy (CBT) is a type of talk therapy that is commonly used to treat anxiety and depression. CBT can help people with schizoaffective disorder to identify and change negative thought patterns and behaviors that contribute to stress and anxiety.

Medication: In some cases, medication may be necessary to manage symptoms of anxiety and stress. Antidepressants and anti-anxiety medications may be prescribed by a doctor to help manage symptoms.

Social support: Having a strong support system can be very helpful in managing stress and anxiety. Talking to friends and family members can help to reduce feelings of isolation and promote a sense of connection and belonging.

It is important to note that everyone is different and what works for one person may not work for another. Therefore, it is important to experiment with different techniques and find what works best for you.

In addition to these techniques, several lifestyle changes can help manage stress and anxiety. These include:

Getting enough sleep: Sleep is essential for managing stress and anxiety. Aim to get at least 7-8 hours of sleep each night.

Eating a healthy diet: A healthy diet can help to reduce stress and anxiety. Avoid caffeine and alcohol, which can increase feelings of anxiety.

Practicing self-care: Self-care activities such as taking a warm bath, listening to music, or reading a book can help reduce stress and anxiety.

Time management: Poor time management can lead to stress and anxiety. Make a schedule and stick to it to help reduce feelings of overwhelm.

Avoiding triggers: Identify your triggers and try to avoid them as much as possible. This may include avoiding stressful situations or people who trigger anxiety.

In conclusion, managing stress and anxiety is an important part of managing schizoaffective disorder. By using a combination of techniques such as relaxation, mindfulness, exercise, CBT, and medication, and making lifestyle changes such as getting enough sleep, eating a healthy diet, and practicing self-care, people with schizoaffective disorder can reduce stress and anxiety and improve their overall quality of life.

Living with Schizoaffective Disorder and Employment

Schizoaffective disorder can have a significant impact on a person's ability to work and maintain employment. However, with proper treatment and support, many individuals with schizoaffective disorder can successfully manage their symptoms and maintain employment. This chapter will discuss the challenges individuals with schizoaffective disorder may face in the workplace and offer tips and strategies for managing symptoms and thriving in the workplace.

Challenges in the Workplace

One of the most significant challenges individuals with schizoaffective disorder may face in the workplace is stigma and discrimination. Unfortunately, mental health conditions such as schizoaffective disorder are often stigmatized, which can lead to discrimination and prejudice in the workplace. This can make it challenging for individuals with schizoaffective disorder to find and maintain employment, as well as progress in their careers.

Another challenge in the workplace is managing symptoms. Schizoaffective disorder can cause a range of symptoms, including hallucinations, delusions, mood swings, and cognitive difficulties. These symptoms can impact an individual's ability to focus, communicate effectively, and complete tasks, which can make it challenging to maintain employment.

Tips and Strategies

Despite these challenges, there are several strategies that individuals with schizoaffective disorder can use to manage their symptoms and thrive in the workplace. Here are some tips and strategies for managing symptoms in the workplace:

Communicate with Your Employer

It's essential to communicate with your employer about your condition and any accommodations you may need. Your employer is legally required to provide reasonable accommodations for your condition under the Americans with Disabilities Act (ADA). Accommodations may include a flexible schedule, a modified work environment, or the use of assistive technology.

Take Care of Your Mental Health

It's crucial to prioritize your mental health by taking medication, attending therapy, and engaging in self-care activities. This can help reduce symptoms and improve your ability to focus and complete tasks in the workplace.

Develop Coping Strategies

Developing coping strategies can help you manage symptoms when they arise in the workplace. Coping strategies may include taking breaks, practicing mindfulness, or seeking support from a colleague or supervisor.

Practice Time Management

Managing time effectively can help you stay on track and complete tasks efficiently. Breaking tasks into smaller, manageable pieces and prioritizing tasks can help you stay organized and reduce stress.

Build a Support System

Having a support system can help you manage symptoms and navigate challenges in the workplace. This may include friends, family members, therapists, or support groups.

Focus on Your Strengths

Focusing on your strengths can help you build confidence and recognize your value in the workplace. Take note of your successes and accomplishments and use them to fuel your motivation and drive.

Conclusion

Schizoaffective disorder can present challenges in the workplace, but with the right support and strategies, individuals with schizoaffective disorder can maintain employment and thrive in their careers. Communication with employers, prioritizing mental health, developing coping strategies, practicing time management, building a support system, and focusing on strengths can all help individuals with schizoaffective disorder overcome workplace challenges and achieve success.

Schizoaffective Disorder and Substance Abuse

Schizoaffective disorder is a complex mental health condition that can significantly impact an individual's life in various ways. One of the most significant challenges faced by individuals with schizoaffective disorder is substance abuse. Substance abuse refers to the use of drugs or alcohol in a way that negatively impacts an individual's physical or mental health, relationships, work, or other aspects of their life. Individuals with schizoaffective disorder are at higher risk of developing substance abuse problems due to various factors, including self-medication, negative symptoms, and impaired judgment.

Substance abuse can worsen the symptoms of schizoaffective disorder and make it more challenging to manage the condition. It can lead to poorer treatment outcomes, increased hospitalization, and a lower quality of life. Additionally, substance abuse can exacerbate the risk of other health problems such as liver disease, lung disease, heart disease, and infectious diseases.

Understanding the connection between schizoaffective disorder and substance abuse is crucial to ensure effective treatment and management of both conditions. Here are some essential things to know about substance abuse in schizoaffective disorder:

Risk Factors for Substance Abuse

Several factors can increase the risk of substance abuse in individuals with schizoaffective disorder. These include:

Self-medication: Some individuals with schizoaffective disorder may turn to drugs or alcohol to self-medicate and alleviate symptoms such as anxiety, depression, or hallucinations.

Impaired judgment: The cognitive symptoms of schizoaffective disorder can affect an individual's ability to make sound decisions, leading them to engage in substance abuse.

Social isolation: The negative symptoms of schizoaffective disorder, such as withdrawal, can lead to social isolation and loneliness, increasing the risk of substance abuse.

History of substance abuse: Individuals with a history of substance abuse are at higher risk of developing substance abuse problems in the future.

Effects of Substance Abuse on Schizoaffective Disorder

Substance abuse can worsen the symptoms of schizoaffective disorder and make it more challenging to manage the condition. It can lead to the following effects:

Increased risk of hospitalization: Substance abuse can increase the frequency and severity of psychotic episodes, leading to more frequent hospitalizations.

Worsening of negative symptoms: Substance abuse can worsen the negative symptoms of schizoaffective disorder, such as apathy, social withdrawal, and lack of motivation.

Poor treatment outcomes: Substance abuse can make it more challenging to manage the symptoms of schizoaffective disorder and reduce the effectiveness of treatments.

Increased risk of suicide: Individuals with schizoaffective disorder who abuse substances are at higher risk of suicidal ideation and attempts.

Treatment for Substance Abuse in Schizoaffective Disorder

Treatment for substance abuse in individuals with schizoaffective disorder typically involves a combination of medication, psychotherapy, and behavioral therapies. Some of the commonly used treatments include:

Medications: Medications such as antipsychotics and antidepressants can help manage the symptoms of schizoaffective disorder and reduce the risk of substance abuse.

Cognitive-behavioral therapy (CBT): CBT can help individuals identify and modify negative thought patterns and behaviors that contribute to substance abuse.

Motivational interviewing: Motivational interviewing is a goal-oriented approach that helps individuals identify and change behaviors that contribute to substance abuse.

Support groups: Support groups such as Alcoholics Anonymous or Narcotics Anonymous can provide a sense of community and support for individuals with substance abuse problems.

Prevention of Substance Abuse in Schizoaffective Disorder

Preventing substance abuse in individuals with schizoaffective disorder involves several strategies, including:

Educating individuals and their families about the risks of substance abuse in schizoaffective disorder.

Healthy Eating Habits for Schizoaffective Disorder

Maintaining a healthy diet is essential for individuals with schizoaffective disorder to manage their physical and mental health. A balanced and nutritious diet can help reduce symptoms and side effects of medication, improve cognitive function, and increase energy levels. In this chapter, we will explore the importance of healthy eating habits and provide tips on how to incorporate them into your daily routine.

Why is healthy eating important for schizoaffective disorder?

There are several reasons why healthy eating habits are essential for individuals with schizoaffective disorder. Firstly, antipsychotic medication, which is often prescribed for this condition, can cause weight gain and other metabolic side effects, such as high blood sugar and cholesterol levels. A healthy diet can help manage these side effects and reduce the risk of developing obesity and other health complications.

Secondly, a balanced diet that includes fruits, vegetables, whole grains, lean protein, and healthy fats can improve cognitive function and reduce symptoms of depression and anxiety. Research has shown that a Mediterranean-style diet, which emphasizes plant-based foods, fish, and olive oil, may be particularly beneficial for individuals with mental health conditions, including schizoaffective disorder.

Finally, a healthy diet can increase energy levels and improve overall wellbeing, making it easier to manage the challenges of daily life with schizoaffective disorder.

Tips for incorporating healthy eating habits

Focus on whole, nutrient-dense foods

Eating a variety of whole, nutrient-dense foods is essential for maintaining good physical and mental health. These include fruits, vegetables, whole grains, lean protein sources, and healthy fats. Avoid processed foods and foods that are high in sugar and saturated fat, as these can exacerbate symptoms and cause weight gain.

Plan meals ahead of time

Planning meals ahead of time can help ensure that you are eating a balanced diet and can make it easier to resist unhealthy food choices. Set aside time each week to plan your meals and make a grocery list, and consider meal prepping or batch cooking to save time during the week.

Eat regular meals and snacks

Skipping meals or going too long without eating can cause blood sugar fluctuations, which can worsen mood symptoms and cause fatigue. Aim to eat regular meals and snacks throughout the day to maintain energy levels and stabilize blood sugar.

Stay hydrated

Drinking plenty of water is important for overall health and can help manage medication side effects, such as constipation. Aim to drink at least eight glasses of water per day, and avoid sugary drinks and alcohol, which can dehydrate the body and exacerbate symptoms.

Consider supplements

Some individuals with schizoaffective disorder may benefit from taking supplements to support their mental and physical health. Omega-3 fatty acids, for example, have been shown to improve cognitive function and reduce symptoms of depression and anxiety. Talk to your healthcare provider before taking any supplements, as they may interact with medication or other health conditions.

In conclusion, maintaining a healthy diet is an essential part of managing schizoaffective disorder. By focusing on whole, nutrient-dense foods, planning meals ahead of time, eating regular meals and snacks, staying hydrated, and considering supplements, individuals with schizoaffective disorder can improve their physical and mental health and overall quality of life. Consult with your healthcare provider or a registered dietitian for more specific dietary recommendations tailored to your individual needs.

Exercise and Physical Activity for Schizoaffective Disorder

Exercise and physical activity can have numerous benefits for individuals living with schizoaffective disorder. Studies have shown that regular exercise can help to reduce symptoms of depression and anxiety, improve mood, increase self-esteem, and promote overall physical health.

Exercise can take many forms, and it is important to find an activity that is enjoyable and sustainable. This could include activities such as walking, jogging, cycling, swimming, dancing, or any other form of physical activity that gets the heart rate up and the body moving.

For individuals living with schizoaffective disorder, it is important to start slowly and gradually increase the intensity and duration of exercise. This can help to avoid injury and prevent feelings of overwhelm or exhaustion. It may also be helpful to work with a healthcare provider or physical therapist to develop a safe and effective exercise routine.

In addition to the physical benefits, exercise can also have positive effects on mental health. Exercise has been shown to increase the production of endorphins, which are chemicals in the brain that can improve mood and reduce feelings of pain and stress. Exercise can also help to reduce levels of the stress hormone cortisol, which can be elevated in individuals with schizoaffective disorder.

It is important to note that exercise should not be used as a substitute for medication or other forms of treatment for schizoaffective disorder. However, it can be a helpful adjunct therapy that can improve overall well-being and reduce symptoms.

In addition to structured exercise, incorporating more physical activity into daily life can also be beneficial. This could include activities such as taking the stairs instead of the elevator, gardening, or playing with pets. These small changes can add up over time and have a positive impact on physical and mental health.

It is also important to consider the role of social support in maintaining an exercise routine. Joining a gym or exercise class can provide a sense of community and accountability, which can help maintain motivation and consistency.

In summary, exercise and physical activity can be a powerful tool for managing symptoms of schizoaffective disorder. Regular exercise can improve mood, reduce stress, and promote overall physical health. It is important to start slowly and gradually increase the intensity and to work with a healthcare provider to develop a safe and effective exercise routine. Incorporating more physical activity into daily life can also be beneficial, and social support can help maintain motivation and consistency.

Yoga and Meditation for Schizoaffective Disorder

Yoga and meditation are increasingly popular practices for improving mental health and well-being. While schizoaffective disorder is a complex and challenging condition, yoga and meditation can provide valuable tools for managing symptoms, reducing stress, and improving overall quality of life.

Yoga is a physical and mental practice that originated in ancient India. It involves a series of postures, breathing techniques, and meditation practices that are designed to promote physical strength, flexibility, and relaxation. In recent years, yoga has become increasingly popular as a form of complementary therapy for mental health conditions.

Meditation is another practice that has been used for thousands of years to improve mental and emotional well-being. It involves training the mind to focus on the present moment, usually by focusing on the breath or a specific object or sound. Meditation has been shown to reduce stress, improve concentration, and promote feelings of calm and relaxation.

Research has shown that yoga and meditation can be beneficial for people with schizoaffective disorder. For example, a study published in the Journal of Psychiatric Research found that eight weeks of yoga practice significantly reduced symptoms of anxiety and depression in people with schizophrenia. Another study published in the Journal of Alternative and Complementary Medicine found that a mindfulness-based stress reduction program improved quality of life and reduced symptoms of anxiety and depression in people with schizophrenia and related disorders.

There are several reasons why yoga and meditation may be helpful for people with schizoaffective disorder. First, both practices can help reduce stress, which is a common trigger for symptoms such as anxiety, depression, and psychosis. Stress reduction techniques such as deep breathing and meditation can help calm the mind and promote feelings of relaxation and well-being.

Second, yoga and meditation can help improve physical health, which can have a positive impact on mental health as well. Yoga has been shown to improve cardiovascular health, reduce inflammation, and boost immune function, all of which can help reduce the risk of chronic health conditions and improve overall well-being. Meditation has also been shown to have physical health benefits, such as reducing blood pressure and improving immune function.

Third, yoga and meditation can help improve self-awareness and self-regulation, which are important skills for managing symptoms of schizoaffective disorder. Both practices involve paying attention to the body and mind and learning to recognize and regulate thoughts, emotions, and physical sensations. This can help people with schizoaffective disorder become more attuned to their own needs and better able to manage symptoms such as anxiety, depression, and mood swings.

If you are interested in trying yoga or meditation to help manage symptoms of schizoaffective disorder, it is important to start slowly and work with a qualified instructor who has experience working with people with mental health conditions. It is also important to talk to your healthcare provider before starting any new exercise or meditation program, especially if you have any medical conditions or are taking medication.

In addition to yoga and meditation, other forms of exercise and physical activity can be beneficial for people with schizoaffective disorder. For example, aerobic exercise such as walking, running, or cycling has been shown to improve mood and reduce symptoms of depression and anxiety. Strength training and other forms of resistance exercise can also be beneficial for improving physical health and reducing stress.

Overall, incorporating yoga, meditation, and other forms of physical activity into a comprehensive treatment plan for schizoaffective disorder can help improve symptoms, reduce stress, and improve overall quality of life. With the guidance of a qualified instructor and the support of a healthcare provider, these practices can be a valuable tool for managing this challenging condition.

Creativity and Schizoaffective Disorder

Schizoaffective disorder is a chronic mental health condition characterized by a combination of symptoms of schizophrenia, such as hallucinations and delusions, and symptoms of mood disorders, such as depression and mania. It can be a challenging condition to live with, as it can affect various aspects of an individual's life, including their relationships, work, and overall wellbeing. However, one area where individuals with schizoaffective disorder may find some relief and comfort is through creativity.

Creativity is a broad term that encompasses various forms of self-expression, such as art, music, writing, dance, and more. Engaging in creative activities can have many benefits for individuals with schizoaffective disorder, such as reducing stress, improving mood, increasing self-esteem, and enhancing overall wellbeing.

One of the primary benefits of creativity for individuals with schizoaffective disorder is its therapeutic value. Creativity can serve as a form of self-expression and a way to process difficult emotions, thoughts, and experiences. It can provide individuals with an outlet for their feelings and enable them to express themselves in a non-verbal way. For instance, painting or drawing can help individuals visualize and express their feelings in a way that words cannot capture.

Music is another form of creativity that can be therapeutic for individuals with schizoaffective disorder. Listening to music can have a calming effect on the mind and body and can reduce stress and anxiety. Playing an instrument or singing can also be beneficial, as it allows individuals to express themselves creatively and can serve as a form of meditation and mindfulness.

Writing is another creative outlet that can be helpful for individuals with schizoaffective disorder. Writing can serve as a way to process difficult emotions and thoughts and can help individuals gain a better understanding of themselves and their condition. It can also serve as a form of self-reflection and can enable individuals to explore their experiences in a more profound and meaningful way.

Dance is another form of creativity that can be beneficial for individuals with schizoaffective disorder. Dancing can improve mood, increase self-esteem, and reduce stress and anxiety. It can also serve as a form of physical exercise, which can have many health benefits, such as reducing the risk of heart disease, diabetes, and other chronic health conditions.

Engaging in creative activities can also provide individuals with a sense of purpose and fulfillment. It can help them feel more connected to their emotions, thoughts, and experiences and can enable them to express themselves in a meaningful way. Creativity can also provide individuals with a sense of accomplishment and can boost their self-esteem.

It is essential to note that while creativity can be beneficial for individuals with schizoaffective disorder, it should not be used as a substitute for professional treatment. Creativity can serve as complementary therapy, and it is essential to seek professional help and adhere to a treatment plan prescribed by a healthcare provider.

In conclusion, creativity can be a powerful tool for individuals with schizoaffective disorder. Engaging in creative activities can provide therapeutic benefits, such as reducing stress and anxiety, improving mood, and enhancing overall wellbeing. Creativity can also serve as a form of self-expression and enable individuals to process difficult emotions and experiences. Overall, creativity can be a valuable addition to a comprehensive treatment plan for individuals with schizoaffective disorder.

Finding Meaning and Purpose in Schizoaffective Disorder

Schizoaffective disorder can be a challenging condition to live with, and it can be difficult to find a sense of meaning and purpose in life when dealing with symptoms such as mood swings, delusions, and hallucinations. However, it is possible to find meaning and purpose in life, even while managing the symptoms of schizoaffective disorder. In this chapter, we will explore ways to find meaning and purpose in life while living with schizoaffective disorder.

One way to find meaning and purpose in life is to set goals for oneself. Goals can give a person direction and help them focus on what they want to achieve. When setting goals, it is important to make them specific, measurable, achievable, relevant, and time-bound. For example, a person with schizoaffective disorder might set a goal of completing a degree, learning a new skill, or starting a business. By setting goals and working towards them, a person can gain a sense of accomplishment and purpose.

Another way to find meaning and purpose in life is to engage in personally meaningful activities. This might include spending time with loved ones, volunteering for a cause, or pursuing a hobby. When choosing activities, it is important to consider one's values and interests and to choose activities that align with those values and interests. For example, a person who values social justice might volunteer for an organization that advocates for human rights, while a person who enjoys art might take a painting class.

Spirituality can also be a source of meaning and purpose for some people. Spirituality can be defined in many ways but generally refers to a sense of connection to something larger than oneself. This might involve participating in religious practices, practicing meditation or yoga, or engaging in nature-based activities. Spirituality can help a person feel connected to the world around them and give them a sense of purpose and meaning.

In addition to setting goals, engaging in meaningful activities, and exploring spirituality, it can be helpful to cultivate a positive mindset. This can involve practicing gratitude, focusing on one's strengths and accomplishments, and reframing negative thoughts. By focusing on the positive, a person can find meaning and purpose in even the most challenging situations.

Another way to find meaning and purpose in life is to connect with others who have similar experiences. This might involve joining a support group for people with schizoaffective disorder, participating in online forums, or attending conferences or workshops. By connecting with others who understand what it's like to live with schizoaffective disorder, a person can feel less isolated and gain a sense of community and belonging.

Finally, it is important to remember that finding meaning and purpose in life is a journey, not a destination. It may take time and effort to discover what gives one's life meaning and purpose, and what works for one person may not work for another. It is important to be patient and persistent and to keep an open mind about the possibilities for finding meaning and purpose in life.

In conclusion, while living with schizoaffective disorder can be challenging, it is possible to find meaning and purpose in life. By setting goals, engaging in meaningful activities, exploring spirituality, cultivating a positive mindset, connecting with others, and being patient and persistent, a person can find a sense of purpose and meaning in life, even while managing the symptoms of schizoaffective disorder.

Managing Suicidal Thoughts and Behavior in Schizoaffective Disorder

Schizoaffective disorder is a complex mental illness that can have significant impacts on an individual's mental health and well-being. One of the most concerning aspects of this disorder is the increased risk of suicidal thoughts and behavior. Research has shown that individuals with schizoaffective disorder are at a higher risk of suicide compared to the general population. This makes it crucial for individuals with this disorder to understand how to manage suicidal thoughts and behaviors.

It is important to remember that having suicidal thoughts does not mean that you are weak or that you are a bad person. It is a symptom of an illness and can be managed with the right treatment and support. If you are experiencing suicidal thoughts, it is essential to seek help immediately.

The first step in managing suicidal thoughts is to create a safety plan. This involves identifying warning signs and creating a plan of action for when these warning signs occur. A safety plan typically includes a list of emergency phone numbers, coping strategies, and a plan for how to stay safe during a crisis.

It is also essential to seek professional help. A mental health professional can work with you to develop coping strategies and provide support during times of crisis. They can also help you to manage any medication or therapy that you are currently undergoing.

If you are experiencing suicidal thoughts, it is important to have a support system. This can include friends, family members, and mental health professionals. It is important to talk openly and honestly with your support system about how you are feeling. They can provide you with emotional support and help you to develop coping strategies.

In addition to seeking professional help and having a support system, several self-care strategies can help manage suicidal thoughts. These can include getting regular exercise, practicing relaxation techniques such as meditation and deep breathing, and eating a healthy and balanced diet. It is also important to avoid alcohol and drugs, which can increase feelings of depression and suicidal thoughts.

It is important to note that managing suicidal thoughts is an ongoing process. It may take time to find the right treatment and coping strategies that work for you. However, with the right support, it is possible to manage these thoughts and live a fulfilling life.

In summary, managing suicidal thoughts and behavior is a crucial part of managing schizoaffective disorder. It is essential to seek professional help, create a safety plan, and have a support system in place. Additionally, practicing self-care strategies and avoiding drugs and alcohol can help manage these thoughts. Remember, suicidal thoughts do not define you and with the right treatment and support, it is possible to live a fulfilling life.

Identifying Triggers for Schizoaffective Disorder

Schizoaffective disorder is a mental illness that combines symptoms of both schizophrenia and mood disorders, such as bipolar disorder or major depression. It can be a challenging condition to manage, and identifying triggers for symptoms is an essential part of effective treatment. Triggers can be anything that sets off symptoms or makes them worse, and they can vary from person to person.

Common triggers for schizoaffective disorder can include stress, substance abuse, changes in sleep patterns, and disruptions in daily routines. Other triggers may include interpersonal conflicts, traumatic events, and certain medications. It is crucial to identify these triggers so that they can be avoided or minimized whenever possible.

One way to identify triggers is to keep a mood and symptom journal. This involves recording any changes in mood, symptoms, and behavior over time. It can be helpful to note the time of day, the specific circumstances, and any thoughts or feelings that may have contributed to the mood or behavior. With time, patterns may emerge that can help identify triggers for symptoms.

It is also important to pay attention to physical sensations that may signal the onset of symptoms. These may include racing thoughts, changes in appetite, feelings of anxiety or agitation, and changes in sleep patterns. Recognizing these physical sensations and addressing them promptly can help prevent symptoms from escalating.

In addition to keeping a mood and symptom journal, it can be helpful to work with a mental health professional to identify triggers and develop coping strategies. A mental health professional can help identify patterns and triggers that may be difficult to recognize on one's own. They can also help develop personalized coping strategies to manage symptoms when they arise.

Coping strategies may include relaxation techniques such as deep breathing, mindfulness, and meditation. Exercise, healthy eating habits, and a regular sleep routine can also help manage symptoms and minimize triggers. Support from friends, family, and mental health professionals can be essential for managing symptoms and maintaining mental health.

In some cases, medication may be necessary to manage symptoms and prevent relapse. A mental health professional can help determine the appropriate medication and dosage based on individual symptoms and medical history. It is essential to follow the prescribed treatment plan and to communicate regularly with the mental health professional about any changes in symptoms or medication side effects.

In conclusion, identifying triggers for schizoaffective disorder is a crucial component of effective treatment. Triggers can vary from person to person and may include stress, substance abuse, changes in sleep patterns, and disruptions in daily routines. Keeping a mood and symptom journal, paying attention to physical sensations, and working with a mental health professional can help identify triggers and develop coping strategies to manage symptoms when they arise. Coping strategies may include relaxation techniques, exercise, healthy eating habits, and medication. With proper identification and management of triggers, individuals with schizoaffective disorder can live full and meaningful lives.

Creating a Crisis Plan for Schizoaffective Disorder

Schizoaffective disorder can be a challenging condition to manage, and it is important to have a plan in place to handle potential crises. One key aspect of this plan is to identify warning signs and triggers that may lead to a crisis and to develop strategies to manage these situations. In this chapter, we will discuss how to create a crisis plan for schizoaffective disorder.

The first step in creating a crisis plan is to identify potential warning signs and triggers. Warning signs are symptoms or changes in behavior that indicate that the individual may be entering a crisis phase. These may include increased anxiety or agitation, a sense of hopelessness or despair, changes in sleep patterns or appetite, and increased isolation or withdrawal from social interactions.

Triggers are external events or situations that may cause the individual to experience an increase in symptoms or to enter a crisis phase. These may include stressors such as work-related problems, financial difficulties, interpersonal conflict, or other life events that may be particularly challenging.

Once warning signs and triggers have been identified, the next step is to develop strategies for managing these situations. This may include identifying coping mechanisms such as breathing exercises, mindfulness meditation, or engaging in a favorite hobby or activity. It may also involve reaching out to support networks, such as family and friends, mental health professionals, or support groups.

In addition to identifying warning signs and triggers and developing coping strategies, it is important to create a crisis plan that outlines specific steps to take in the event of a crisis. This plan should include emergency contact information for mental health professionals, crisis hotlines, and other resources that may help manage the situation.

The crisis plan should also outline specific steps to take in the event of a crisis, including when and how to contact mental health professionals or emergency services, how to access medication or other treatments, and how to communicate with family and friends about the situation.

It may also be helpful to identify a support person or group who can assist in implementing the crisis plan. This person or group may be a family member, friend, or mental health professional who can provide emotional support and help implement the strategies outlined in the crisis plan.

In addition to creating a crisis plan, it is important to regularly review and update the plan as needed. This may involve revisiting warning signs and triggers, identifying new coping strategies, and adjusting emergency contact information or other details as necessary.

Creating a crisis plan can be a valuable tool for managing schizoaffective disorder, and can help individuals and their support networks feel more prepared and confident in managing potential crises. By identifying warning signs and triggers, developing coping strategies, and outlining specific steps to take in the event of a crisis, individuals can feel more empowered and better able to manage their condition over the long term.

Safety Planning for Schizoaffective Disorder

Living with schizoaffective disorder can be a challenging experience, particularly when it comes to managing symptoms like delusions, hallucinations, and mood swings. As a result, individuals with schizoaffective disorder must have a safety plan in place to help them manage these symptoms and avoid harm.

A safety plan is a personalized, step-by-step guide that outlines what to do when a person experiences a crisis or feels overwhelmed by their symptoms. This plan can include strategies for managing symptoms, contact information for emergency services or crisis hotlines, and a list of people to contact for support.

Here are some key steps to consider when creating a safety plan for schizoaffective disorder:

Identify triggers: The first step in creating a safety plan is to identify potential triggers that may exacerbate symptoms. These triggers may include stress, substance use, social isolation, or changes in medication. By identifying triggers, individuals can take steps to avoid or minimize them.

Develop coping strategies: Once triggers have been identified, it is important to develop coping strategies to manage symptoms when they arise. Coping strategies can include relaxation techniques, mindfulness exercises, or distraction techniques like listening to music or engaging in a hobby. Developing coping strategies can help individuals feel more in control of their symptoms and reduce the likelihood of a crisis.

Create a support network: A strong support network is essential for managing schizoaffective disorder. This network may include family members, friends, mental health professionals, or support groups. Identifying trusted individuals who can provide support during a crisis can be a key part of a safety plan.

Create an emergency plan: In the event of a crisis, it is important to have a clear plan in place. This plan may include contact information for emergency services or crisis hotlines, as well as a list of people to contact for support. Having this information readily available can help individuals act quickly and get the help they need.

Review and update regularly: A safety plan should be reviewed and updated regularly to ensure it remains relevant and effective. As symptoms and triggers may change over time, it is important to regularly reassess and adjust the plan as needed.

In addition to creating a safety plan, individuals with schizoaffective disorder may also benefit from learning and practicing self-care techniques, such as getting enough sleep, eating a balanced diet, and engaging in regular exercise or physical activity. It is also important to attend regular therapy sessions and take any prescribed medication as directed by a healthcare provider.

In conclusion, creating a safety plan for schizoaffective disorder can help individuals manage symptoms, avoid crises, and feel more in control of their mental health. By identifying triggers, developing coping strategies, creating a support network, and having an emergency plan in place, individuals can take steps to stay safe and manage their symptoms effectively. Regular review and updating of the safety plan can help ensure it remains effective and relevant over time.

When dealing with a complex mental illness like schizoaffective disorder, finding the right mental health professional can be a critical part of the recovery process. Schizoaffective disorder requires specialized knowledge and expertise, so it is important to work with someone who is experienced in treating this condition.

There are a variety of mental health professionals who can provide treatment for schizoaffective disorder, including psychiatrists, psychologists, social workers, and counselors. Each of these professionals has a different level of training and expertise, so it is important to choose the right one based on your individual needs and preferences.

Psychiatrists are medical doctors who specialize in the treatment of mental illness. They are trained to diagnose and treat a wide range of psychiatric conditions, including schizoaffective disorder. Psychiatrists can prescribe medication, which is often an important part of the treatment for schizoaffective disorder. They may also provide therapy or refer patients to other mental health professionals for additional treatment.

Psychologists are trained to diagnose and treat mental health conditions, including schizoaffective disorder, using a variety of therapies, such as cognitive behavioral therapy, dialectical behavior therapy, and family therapy. They are not medical doctors and cannot prescribe medication, but they are experts in providing therapy and helping patients manage their symptoms.

Social workers are mental health professionals who help patients with social and emotional issues related to their mental health. They can provide therapy and support services, such as helping patients find housing, employment, or other resources that can help them manage their condition. Social workers may also refer patients to other mental health professionals for additional treatment.

Counselors are mental health professionals who specialize in providing counseling and therapy to individuals and families. They may provide individual, group, or family therapy to help patients manage their symptoms and improve their quality of life. Counselors may also refer patients to other mental health professionals for additional treatment.

When looking for a mental health professional to treat schizoaffective disorder, it is important to consider several factors. These include:

Credentials and experience: Look for a mental health professional who has experience treating schizoaffective disorder and is licensed and certified in their field.

Treatment philosophy: Choose a mental health professional who aligns with your treatment goals and approach to mental health care.

Availability and accessibility: Consider the location and availability of the mental health professional, as well as their ability to provide services in a language or format that is accessible to you.

Insurance coverage: Check with your insurance provider to see which mental health professionals are covered under your plan.

It is important to take the time to find the right mental health professional for you. You may need to try several different providers before finding one who is a good fit. Don't be afraid to ask questions and communicate your needs and preferences to your provider. Building a trusting and supportive relationship with your mental health professional can be an important part of your recovery journey.

Seeking Help in a Crisis for Schizoaffective Disorder

Schizoaffective disorder is a complex mental health condition that requires ongoing management and support. Even with a treatment plan in place, individuals with schizoaffective disorder may experience a crisis at some point. It is essential to have a plan in place for these situations and to know how to seek help when it is needed.

A crisis related to schizoaffective disorder may involve a sudden worsening of symptoms, such as hallucinations or delusions, suicidal ideation or behavior, or a significant change in mood. These situations can be very distressing, not only for the individual with schizoaffective disorder but also for their loved ones. Knowing how to handle these situations can help individuals with schizoaffective disorder feel more in control and less overwhelmed.

The first step in creating a plan for a crisis related to schizoaffective disorder is to work with a mental health professional to develop a personalized crisis plan. This plan should include a list of symptoms that may indicate a crisis is occurring and steps to take when those symptoms arise. The plan should also include a list of emergency contacts, including crisis hotlines, mental health professionals, and family members or friends who can offer support.

It is essential to have a crisis plan that is tailored to the individual's specific needs and preferences. The plan should also be regularly reviewed and updated as needed to ensure that it remains relevant and effective.

When a crisis related to schizoaffective disorder does occur, it is crucial to seek help immediately. Some situations may require immediate medical attention, such as if the individual is experiencing severe suicidal ideation or behavior. In these situations, it may be necessary to call emergency services or go to the emergency room.

If the crisis is not immediately life-threatening, the individual may still need to seek help from a mental health professional. This may involve contacting their therapist or psychiatrist for an emergency appointment or contacting a crisis hotline for support and guidance.

It is important to remember that seeking help during a crisis related to schizoaffective disorder is not a sign of weakness. It takes strength and courage to ask for help when it is needed, and doing so can help individuals with schizoaffective disorder manage their symptoms and feel more in control of their lives.

In addition to seeking professional help, there are also some steps that individuals with schizoaffective disorder can take to manage their symptoms during a crisis. These may include practicing relaxation techniques such as deep breathing or meditation, engaging in physical activity, or taking prescribed medications as directed.

It can also be helpful to reach out to friends or family members for support during a crisis. Having a trusted support system can provide individuals with schizoaffective disorder with the emotional support they need to manage their symptoms and navigate the crisis.

In conclusion, managing a crisis related to schizoaffective disorder requires a combination of preparedness, support, and professional help. By developing a personalized crisis plan and knowing how to seek help when it is needed, individuals with schizoaffective disorder can feel more in control of their symptoms and their lives. It is also essential to remember that seeking help during a crisis is a sign of strength, not weakness, and can lead to improved mental health outcomes.

Navigating the Mental Health System with Schizoaffective Disorder

Navigating the mental health system can be overwhelming for individuals with Schizoaffective Disorder. It is essential to understand the different mental health professionals, treatment options, and available resources to access the best possible care. In this chapter, we will discuss how to navigate the mental health system with Schizoaffective Disorder.

Understanding Mental Health Professionals

Various mental health professionals can assist individuals with Schizoaffective Disorder. These professionals have different levels of education, training, and specialties. Some common mental health professionals include:

Psychiatrists: Psychiatrists are medical doctors who specialize in mental health. They can diagnose and treat mental health conditions and prescribe medications.

Psychologists: Psychologists hold a doctoral degree in psychology and provide psychotherapy services to individuals with mental health conditions. Psychologists are not medical doctors and cannot prescribe medication.

Social workers: Social workers have a master's degree in social work and provide counseling services to individuals with mental health conditions. They can also provide case management services to connect individuals with other community resources.

Licensed Professional Counselors: Licensed Professional Counselors (LPC) hold a master's degree in counseling and provide counseling services to individuals with mental health conditions.

Psychiatric nurses: Psychiatric nurses have a nursing degree and specialize in mental health. They work with psychiatrists to provide medication management and assist with the overall treatment plan.

Choosing the Right Mental Health Professional

When choosing a mental health professional, it is essential to consider their education, experience, and specialties. Individuals with Schizoaffective Disorder may benefit from a mental health professional who has experience working with individuals with this condition. It is also important to consider the type of treatment that the mental health professional offers and if it aligns with the individual's needs.

Accessing Treatment

There are various treatment options available for individuals with Schizoaffective Disorder, including medication, therapy, and support groups. It is important to work with a mental health professional to determine the best treatment plan.

Medication: Medication can help manage symptoms of Schizoaffective Disorder. A psychiatrist can prescribe medication and monitor its effectiveness. It is essential to take medication as prescribed and report any side effects to the psychiatrist.

Therapy: Therapy can help individuals with Schizoaffective Disorder manage symptoms and improve their overall well-being. Cognitive Behavioral Therapy (CBT) and Dialectical Behavioral Therapy (DBT) are two therapy options that can be beneficial for individuals with Schizoaffective Disorder.

Support Groups: Support groups can provide individuals with Schizoaffective Disorder with a safe space to discuss their experiences and connect with others who have similar experiences. NAMI (National Alliance on Mental Illness) offers support groups for individuals with Schizoaffective Disorder.

Accessing Resources

There are various resources available to individuals with Schizoaffective Disorder and their families. Some of these resources include:

National Alliance on Mental Illness (NAMI): NAMI is a nonprofit organization that provides education, advocacy, and support to individuals with mental illness and their families.

Substance Abuse and Mental Health Services Administration (SAMHSA): SAMHSA is a government agency that provides information and resources for individuals with mental illness and substance use disorders.

Mental Health America: Mental Health America is a nonprofit organization that provides education and advocacy for individuals with mental illness.

Social Security Administration: The Social Security Administration offers disability benefits for individuals with mental illness who are unable to work.

Health Insurance: Health insurance can help cover the cost of mental health treatment. It is essential to understand what mental health services are covered under the insurance plan.

Conclusion

Navigating the mental health system can be overwhelming for individuals with Schizoaffective Disorder. It is essential to understand the different mental health professionals, treatment options

Peer support can be an essential component of recovery for people living with schizoaffective disorder. Schizoaffective disorder can be a challenging and isolating condition, but connecting with others who have similar experiences can provide a sense of community, reduce feelings of isolation, and offer practical support and advice. Peer support can be particularly valuable for individuals who may not have access to mental health services or who feel stigmatized by their diagnosis.

What is Peer Support?

Peer support is a form of support that is provided by people with similar experiences or challenges. It is based on the belief that people who have faced similar challenges and difficulties can offer valuable insights, advice, and empathy. Peer support can take many different forms, including self-help groups, peer counseling, and peer mentoring. Peer support can be particularly helpful for individuals who are seeking a sense of community, validation, and a space to share their experiences.

Benefits of Peer Support for Schizoaffective Disorder

Connecting with peers who have similar experiences can be an important part of recovery for individuals living with schizoaffective disorder. Some of the benefits of peer support include:

Community: Peer support provides a sense of community and belonging. Individuals with schizoaffective disorder may feel isolated or stigmatized by their diagnosis. Connecting with others who have similar experiences can provide a sense of belonging and reduce feelings of isolation.

Validation: Peer support can provide validation and understanding. Individuals with schizoaffective disorder may feel misunderstood or judged by others who do not have experience with mental illness. Peer support offers a space to share experiences, feelings, and challenges with people who understand and can offer empathy and support.

Practical support: Peer support can offer practical advice and support. Peers can provide information about local resources, share coping strategies, and offer advice on navigating the mental health system.

Role models: Peer support can provide role models for recovery. Seeing others who have successfully managed their condition and are living fulfilling lives can offer hope and inspiration.

Self-esteem: Peer support can improve self-esteem and confidence. Connecting with others who have similar experiences and challenges can help individuals feel less alone and more confident in managing their condition.

Types of Peer Support

There are many different types of peer support available for individuals with schizoaffective disorder. Some of the most common types include:

Self-help groups: Self-help groups are peer-led groups where individuals with similar experiences can connect and share their experiences. These groups are often free or low-cost and can be found through local mental health organizations or online.

Peer mentoring: Peer mentoring involves connecting with a mentor who has experience living with schizoaffective disorder. Mentors can offer practical advice and support and can act as role models for recovery.

Peer counseling: Peer counseling involves connecting with a trained peer counselor who has experience living with schizoaffective disorder. Peer counselors can offer emotional support, and practical advice, and can act as a sounding board for concerns or challenges.

Online forums: Online forums and support groups provide a space for individuals to connect with others who have similar experiences. These groups can offer a sense of community and support for individuals who may not have access to local peer support groups.

How to Find Peer Support

Finding peer support can be a challenging process, but there are many resources available. Some tips for finding peer support include:

Talk to a mental health professional: Mental health professionals can provide information about local peer support groups and resources.

Search online: Many peer support groups have online forums or social media groups. Searching online for "schizoaffective disorder peer support" can provide a starting point.

Reach out to local mental health organizations: Local mental health organizations may offer peer support groups or have information about other resources.

Moving Forward with Hope and Resilience in Schizoaffective Disorder
Schizoaffective disorder can be a challenging and complex mental illness to manage, but with the right tools, resources, and support, it is possible to move forward with hope and resilience. In this chapter, we will discuss some key strategies for building resilience and maintaining hope while living with schizoaffective disorder.

One important aspect of moving forward with hope and resilience is acknowledging that recovery is possible. While schizoaffective disorder is a chronic condition, it is not a life sentence. With the right treatment, therapy, and support, individuals with schizoaffective disorder can live meaningful and fulfilling lives. It is important to remember that recovery looks different for everyone and that progress can be slow and incremental. Celebrate the small victories along the way and focus on your unique path to wellness.

Another important aspect of moving forward with hope and resilience is building a strong support network. This can include family, friends, mental health professionals, support groups, and peer support networks. Having people to turn to during difficult times can make all the difference in maintaining hope and resilience. If you don't already have a support network, consider joining a local support group or reaching out to an online community for people with schizoaffective disorder.

Self-care is also a key component of moving forward with hope and resilience. This can include eating a healthy diet, getting enough sleep, engaging in regular exercise, and finding activities that bring you joy and fulfillment. Engaging in creative activities, such as art, music, or writing, can also be a powerful way to cope with symptoms and maintain a sense of purpose and meaning.

Another important strategy for maintaining hope and resilience is learning to manage stress and anxiety. Mindfulness practices, such as meditation or yoga, can be effective tools for reducing stress and promoting relaxation. It is also important to develop coping skills for managing symptoms when they arise. This may include grounding techniques, breathing exercises, or other mindfulness practices.

Finally, it is important to work with your mental health team to develop a personalized treatment plan that is tailored to your individual needs and goals. This may include medication, therapy, or a combination of both. It is important to be honest with your mental health professionals about your symptoms, challenges, and goals so that they can work with you to create a plan that is right for you.

Living with schizoaffective disorder can be challenging, but it is important to remember that recovery is possible. By building a strong support network, practicing self-care, and working with your mental health team, you can move forward with hope and resilience. Remember to be patient with yourself and celebrate the small victories along the way. With time, patience, and perseverance, you can create a fulfilling and meaningful life despite the challenges of schizoaffective disorder.

Printed in the USA
CPSIA information can be obtained
at www.ICGtesting.com
LVHW100154300823
756706LV00007B/220

9 789357 333303